WILD GIRL, WILD BOY

A PLAY

Copyright © David Almond 2002, 2006

First published by Hodder Children's Books, 2002.
First published in the Hodder Literature series, 2006, by Hodder Murray, an imprint of
Hodder Education, a member of the Hodder Headline Group, 338 Euston Road,
London NW1 3BH.

The right of David Almond to be identified as the author of this work has been
asserted by him in accordance with the Copyright, Designs and Patents Act 1988.

Impression number   10 9 8 7 6 5 4 3 2
Year   2011 2010

ISBN-10   0 340 90792 4
ISBN-13   978 0 340 90792 4

A catalogue record for this title is available from the British Library

Typeset in Bembo by Servis Filmsetting Limited, Manchester.
Printed in Great Britain by CPI Antony Rowe, Chippenham, Wiltshire.

Orders: please contact Bookpoint Ltd, 130 Milton Park, Abingdon, Oxon OX14 4SB.
Telephone: (44) 01235 827720. Fax: (44) 01235 400454. Lines are open from
9.00 am to 6.00 pm, Monday to Saturday, with a 24-hour message answering service.
Visit our website at www.hoddereducation.co.uk

David Almond

Wild Girl, Wild Boy
A Play

HODDER LITERATURE

www.hodderliterature.co.uk

If you enjoy *Wild Girl, Wild Boy*, you might enjoy these other books in the Hodder Literature series:

Skellig: The Play by David Almond

Dramatisation of Michael's discovery in the ramshackle garage of his new house of Skellig – part owl and part angel – who may be able to save Michael's dying baby sister, as long as someone else can save Skellig first.

ISBN 0 340 90555 7

Half-caste and Other Poems
by John Agard

A powerful and thought-provoking collection of poetry ideal for exploring cross-cultural themes and poetic form in Key Stages 3 and 4.

ISBN 0 340 92585 X

Shadow of the Beast by Maggie Pearson

The intertwined story of Troy's recovery from a devastating car crash and his reliving of the Beowulf legend as he struggles to come to terms with the death of his father.

ISBN 0 340 89988 3

Exclusive to Hodder Murray

Skellig by David Almond

In the ramshackle garage of his new house, Michael finds Skellig – part owl and part angel – who may be able to save Michael's dying baby sister, as long as someone can save Skellig first.

ISBN 0 340 90554 9

To order *Wild Girl, Wild Boy* or any of the other books in the Hodder Literature series, please contact Bookpoint on 01235 827720. Visit the Hodder Literature website at www.hodderliterature.co.uk.

PREFACE

This is the tale of Elaine Grew, a brave and troubled young soul. She lives with her mother in an estate on the edge of a northern city. Outside the estate is an open hillside, a group or allotments, a lark-filled sky. Elaine has been happy here, but last year her dad died and now Elaine's in turmoil. She can't think straight, she can't see straight, she can't read or write. She squabbles and fights with her mother, who fears that Elaine is losing her mind, that she's losing touch with the world. Elaine's neighbours and school mates turn away from her. They mock her and scorn her and even fear her. Her teachers don't know what to do with her. Elaine begins to stay away from school. She spends day after day in the wilderness of her dad's old allotment. She crawls like a lizard on the earth as she used to when he was with her. She slithers like a snake through the thorns and weeds. She works spells with spiders and digs in the earth for magic seeds.

What is she searching for? What will she find in the overgrown allotment, this place of memories, dreams and enchantment? And who is this wild boy, who watches her, and begins to move towards her?

For Mike Dalton

Wild Girl, Wild Boy was commissioned by the Lyric Theatre, Hammersmith, and the Pop-Up Theatre Company.

The play was first performed at the Lyric Theatre Hammersmith, London on 10th February 2001 in association with the Pop-Up Theatre Company, directed by Michael Dalton, with the following cast:

Elaine – Janet Bamford
McNamara/Doctor – Mark Huckett
Wild Boy/Father – Andrew Oliver
Mother – Mandy Vernon-Smith

Director – Michael Dalton
Assistant Director – Jane Wolfson
Designer – Will Hargreaves
Music – Ransom Notes
Co-Musical Directors – James Hesford
Mark Pearson
Lighting Designer – Ace McCarron
Company Stage Manager – Emma Barron
Set Construction – Set Up Scenery
Dialect Coach – Majella Hurley

The play received a Sainsbury's Checkout Theatre Award.

CHARACTERS

Elaine Grew, a girl

Elaine's mother

Elaine's father

Mr McNamara, a neighbour

The Wild Boy, also called Skoosh

A doctor

A chorus of voices – these are the voices of school mates, teachers, neighbours. These voices provide a cruel commentary that echoes around inside Elaine's head.

SCENE ONE

ELAINE'S bedroom. Daytime. Bright blue sky is visible through the window. There is an untidy bed, a table, a chair. She is at a table, trying to write. On the table are pens and pencils, paper and notebooks. There are sheets of drawings, paintings and scribblings scattered on the table and floor. Pictures of birds and animals are pinned to the wall. A shelf on the wall holds pots of paints. Elaine's canvas shoulder bag hangs from her chair.

ELAINE   Wild ... Girl ... Wild ... Boy ... That's the title. Good. That's the title. Once ... there ... was ... a ... girl ... called ... Elaine ... Ah. Yes. Phew. That's the start ... She ... lived ... with ...

She holds up the paper and looks at her words.

ELAINE   Look at it! Look at it! I'm so stupid. No, I'm not! I have problems ... writing. Something to do with the way I ... see or something.

She looks around, peers into space, as if she's searching for something.

ELAINE   Wild Boy? Wild Boy? He's gone.

1

He was here, and now he's
gone.

She goes to the window and peers out.

ELAINE   Wild Boy! Where are you?
Skoooooosh!
He was here, and now he's gone.

She rattles the window, rattles the door.

ELAINE   Let me out! Let me out!

MUM (*from outside the room*)
Elaine! Elaine, just calm down,
love!

ELAINE   Let me out!

MUM   Oh, Elaine. Be a good girl, will
you?

ELAINE   Ha, a good girl. That's my mum.
She doesn't understand. She
doesn't see. She's locked me in.
Let me out!

ELAINE writes again.

ELAINE   She lived with ... Agh! Words on
me fingers and on stupid paper
slither and crawl and slip and slide
and stagger like wounded things.

2

Look at them. But words on me
tongue can dance and sing like
larky birds. So I'll tell it to you in
dancing words and show it you in
moving pictures. And I'll tell it to
me rattle as well. This is me rattle
I've had since I was small.

ELAINE takes a big seedhead out of her canvas bag.

ELAINE   A seedhead. A present from me
dad. Rattle, rattle. Rattle, rattle.
You'll wake the dead, me mum
used to say. You'll bring the house
down, girl. But she used to sing to
it as well. And Dad was there then,
and we were so happy! You should
have seen the way we went on –
specially me and Dad. The way we
danced! We were so happy!

*ELAINE shakes the seedhead. She dances. The sound and
the dance lead her back into the past, into her memories,
into the allotment. At moments like this, her bedroom and
her dad's allotment merge.*
MUM and DAD enter.
DAD comes to ELAINE and joins in with her dance.

MUM   You two! I don't know what I'll
do with you. You're daft as each
other!

3

DAD holds some raspberries in his open hands. He holds out a raspberry towards ELAINE'S mouth.

DAD   Look at this, love. Taste it. It's from deep in the heart of the garden, deep in the thorns.

ELAINE   It's a raspberry!

ELAINE takes the raspberry, eats it.

DAD   A raspberry. Delicious and wild. Oh, watch the juice! Lick it off!

They laugh at the juice and the stains.
DAD holds out a raspberry to MUM.

DAD   Come on. Taste it, love. That's right.

MUM takes a raspberry, eats it.

MUM   So sweet.

DAD   Delicious and sweet and wild. Come on. Let yourself go. Let's go wild!

ELAINE   Dance Dad, dance!

They all dance happily, then they stutter to a halt.
They are dejected, exhausted.
DAD exits, leaving MUM and ELAINE alone.

4

MUM and ELAINE wipe the juice off their faces.
MUM exits.

ELAINE   Then he died, and there was
nothing more to dance for and
nothing more to sing for.
Let me out!
No answer.

ELAINE is back in the present, alone, in her bedroom.
She puts away her writing things.

ELAINE   Chuck this mess away. This is me.
My name is Elaine. Elaine Grew.
This is the story of my Wild Boy.
And he's gone, but it's true.

She digs down into her canvas bag. She lifts some pictures from the table.

ELAINE   Look, there's things to show it
really happened. Here's the lock
of hair I cut when he was fast
asleep. Here's the pictures he
drew to show the things that he
can see and we can't see ... That I
can't see. In me head's the weird
voice, the way he sang.

She sings weirdly.

5

ELAINE   On me hands is the weird touch
of him. In me memory is the
weird weird story of him. Keep
watching. Keep looking. Keep
listening. It starts way back,
months back, in a time of doom
and gloom and tribulation. Me
dad was six months dead. Me
lovely dad.

She sings, and shakes the seedhead.

ELAINE   It never woke him.

She shakes the seedhead.

ELAINE   Look. This is what it was like.

*She shakes the seedhead, dances, and she is carried again
into the past.*
*This time she is in her bedroom, soon after her dad
has died.*

MUM   Elaine! Elaine!

*MUM enters. ELAINE rattles her seedhead, sings and dances
wildly.*

MUM   Elaine! How many times do I
have to tell you?

They struggle over the seedhead.

6

MUM	You're driving me insane, lass!
ELAINE	Leave me alone! Gerroff me!

ELAINE retreats to a corner.

MUM	Look at us. We were so happy.
ELAINE	I was never happy!
MUM	And you were such a lovely girl.
ELAINE	I was never lovely. I've always been stupid stupid stupid.
MUM	The school's been on the phone again. You've got to go in every day, Elaine, or we'll be in court before we know it, and what'll that lead to?
ELAINE	School! School! Full of doolies and dipsticks just like me.
MUM	Don't say dooley. You're my lovely girl, Elaine.

ELAINE rattles the seedhead, dances and sings.

ELAINE	Rattle rattle! Dooley dipstick thicko dense. Can't read, can't write, can't see straight, can't think straight, can't …
MUM	Oh, Elaine!

ELAINE Can't … anything. Rattle rattle.
Can't even wake the dead!

MUM STOP … THAT … NOISE!

MUM exits.
ELAINE shakes the seedhead more slowly.
We move back into the bedroom in the present.

ELAINE Aye, we started to fight like
that. Fight like cat and dog and
cry like babies and run off
from each other and hide in
corners from each other … So
awful.

ELAINE takes a drawing from the table.

ELAINE I'm good at drawing. This is a
picture I did of me dad. Ages
back. I did it in his allotment.
Laid the paper on a cold frame
and drew him as he worked.
There he is, leaning over the
earth and the sun shining down
and the sky so blue and the
larkybirds singing singing high
above.

*She softly shakes the seedhead. It carries her back into the
past, to the allotment.*

DAD enters, whistling softly.
ELAINE leans over her picture, as if drawing it again.
DAD crouches, picks a broken eggshell from the earth.

DAD   Come and see.

ELAINE   What?

DAD   Come and see, love.

ELAINE goes to him.

ELAINE   What is it?

DAD   A lark's egg. See? Speckled white
                   outside. And brilliant white
                   inside. A chick came out from
                   this. Can you believe it? A little
                   chick made from a yellow yolk
                   and a salty white that'll one day
                   soon be flying over us and
                   singing the loveliest of songs.
                   A miracle. Look! Larks, larks,
                   larks.

They stare into the sky, towards the larks.

ELAINE   Can hardly see them, Dad.

DAD   That's right. They fly that high
                   they nearly disappear. They fly
                   that high you think they fly right
                   out of the world. But listen.

9

Listen to their wild sweet song.
There they are.

They listen, and the larks sing.

DAD That's a lovely picture. How
about putting me name on it, eh?
Go on, it'll be OK. I'll help you.

DAD guides her hand as they form the letters together.

DAD D ... A ... D. That's right. Dad.
Well done. Now put your name
as the artist. E ... L ... A ... I ...
N ... E. Elaine. See? There's you
and me both written down.

ELAINE Dad. Elaine.

DAD One day soon, we'll have your
writing clear as your drawing, eh?
Hey. Let's cut some of those
massive daisies for your
mum. Whoops! Spider.

DAD suddenly plucks something from the air.

DAD You can work spells with these.
Listen.
Spider spider spin your web
Spider spin around my head
Spider spider sit dead still

10

Spider bring me what I will.
A five-pound note!

DAD flourishes a five-pound note.

DAD   It worked!

ELAINE   Silly!

DAD crouches, as if tending to his plants.
ELAINE softly rattles. She dreams and wonders as her
mind moves between the present and the past.

ELAINE   I've got the picture still. Dad.
                           Elaine. Dad. Elaine. Looks a mess,
                           but I knew what it meant ...
                           The allotment. It was a wild
                           place, a wilderness, and I was his
                           wild girl. The middle of it was all
                           tame and neat, but all around: the
                           long grass, the high weeds, where
                           I crawled and wandered and got
                           lost and called out to him.

DAD   Go on, little one.

ELAINE   What, Dad?

DAD   Go on. Crawl deep into the
                           wilderness. Go on. Get lost in
                           there. Go on. I'll be here. Just call
                           out if you get lost and I'll bring
                           you back to me.

ELAINE crawls and laughs and moves through the wilderness of tall grasses and weeds. She sits up and smiles as she remembers.

ELAINE   The allotment. Place of dreams and magic mixed with leeks and spuds and raspberries ever since I was a little little girl. Crawl crawl I went, like a little lizard, crawl crawl like a little snake. Seeds in me eyes and nose, soil on me hands and knees. Crawling crawling further and further into the wild till me dad called—

DAD   Elaine! Wild girl! Time to come back out!

ELAINE   Yes, Dad!

She shakes the seedhead softly. She dreams and wonders.

ELAINE   Rattle rattle. Rattle rattle. Rattle rattle ... There was often someone else there, too. Another man.

McNAMARA enters, stands peering from his own allotment.

ELAINE   McNamara. Had the allotment next to Dad's. Beady eyes, beady stare. Always watching us, he was,

always sneering at us. His place
was all neat and trim with peas
and beans and onions in neat trim
rows.

McNAMARA   Look at it. Look at the state of it.
Like a damn jungle. Hey! What if
we all let our gardens go like that,
eh?

DAD   Eh?

McNAMARA   I said, what if we all let our
gardens go like that? Get it tidied
up, man.

DAD   It's tidy enough for us.

McNAMARA   Eh? And what about the effect
you're having on that poor lass?

DAD   There's nothing wrong with
her.

McNAMARA   Nothing wrong! She'll turn out
daft as you are. Poor girl.

ELAINE   Usually he said nothing, just
watched, just stared. Leaned on
his fence and sneered and stared
and shook his head and clicked
his tongue and stared and stared
and stared.

13

MCNAMARA shakes his head and clicks his tongue and exits.

DAD   I ever show you how to grow a
                 fairy, pet?

ELAINE   A fairy, Daddy?

DAD   A fairy.

ELAINE   There's no such thing as fairies!

DAD   Yes, there is. But nobody knows
                 you got to grow them first, like
                 they was leeks or raspberries. A
                 bit of horse muck'll help, and a
                 bit of spit.

DAD plucks a fairy seed from the air. He holds it on his palm.

DAD   Look! Here's a fairy seed. Spit on
                 it.

They spit together on the fairy seed.

DAD   Whisper a spell:
                 Come along my little fairy, grow
                 like mushroom, grow like magic,
                 grow like happiness in the
                 heart …

ELAINE   Silly!

14

DAD   Put it gently on the ground.

DAD puts the fairy seed on the earth, puts horse muck and water on it.

DAD   Then the horse muck. Then the water. Then spit again.

They spit again.

DAD   Then just wait.

ELAINE   How long?

DAD   That's the mystery. You can never tell. Some fairies take ninety-nine years to grow …

ELAINE   Ninety-nine years!

DAD   And some just take ninety-nine minutes. Or ninety-nine days. Or ninety-nine blinks of an eye. Go on, blink ninety-nine times, keep on wishing, and see if the fairy grows.

They blink and count quickly together and end up in laughter.

DAD   Not enough. No fairy. Ah, well. Mebbe this one's a ninety-nine yearer.

ELAINE   Silly!

DAD exits.
ELAINE softly shakes the seedhead.
She wonders and dreams, and moves between the present and the past.

ELAINE   We had fairies planted
                 everywhere in Dad's allotment.
                 All we ever got of course was
                 spuds and leeks and raspberries.
                 Except each night when the
                 fairies jumped out of the earth
                 and danced like wind and fire in
                 me dreams. I used to draw them,
                 draw me dreams. Fairies!

MCNAMARA enters.
ELAINE is drawn back into the past, into the allotment.
He watches her, shakes his head, clicks his tongue.

MCNAMARA   Fairies! Ha! Ha! He's leading you
                 astray, little lady. He doesn't want
                 you to grow up. He's turning you
                 into a little stupid wild thing.

ELAINE   No, he's not! No, he's not!

MCNAMARA exits.

ELAINE   Was it silly? Was it baby stuff?
                 That's what Mum said. That's

16

what they all said. Their voices
were all around me. Their voices
echoed through my head.

*ELAINE holds her hands around her head as the voices
start.*

SCENE TWO

THE CHORUS OF VOICES

(They are the voices of neighbours, schoolmates and teachers.)

– Have you seen the way she just stares out the window with her gob hanging open?

– Like she's catching flies.

– Like a little kid.

– Like a baby.

– And the state of her books?

– Like a spider's crawled over them.

– Like somebody's chucked spaghetti on them.

– Hey, Elaine, has somebody chucked spaghetti on your book?

– No, that's her writing, man!

– Now leave Elaine alone. Oh dear, Elaine. We're going to have to do better than that, aren't we?

– Concentrate, girl!

18

– Keep your mind on your work.

– Elaine has severe difficulty in maintaining concentration on the task in hand.

– Reading: accuracy?

– Nil.

– Comprehension?

– Nil.

– Reading age?

– Elaine has not yet achieved a score in our current methods of assessment.

– Writing skills?

– Hahahahahahaha!

– She's just out of it, man.

– Round the bend.

– Up the pole.

– Doolally.

– She's upset, man. She's in grief.

– Why's that, then?

– Her dad …

19

               – He was a one, eh?

               – Aye, I know, but he died, didn't he?

               – Aye.

               – Poor soul, eh?

               – Aye, poor soul.

               – Aye.

               – Hey. Listen: Dad's dead and she's losing her head.

               – Dad's dead and you're losing your head,

               – Dad's dead and you're losing your head,

               – Dad's dead and you're …

ELAINE   Stop it! Stop it! Stop it!

MUM comes in, hurries to comfort ELAINE.

MUM   Oh, Elaine, take no notice of them, love.

MUM holds ELAINE tight, then holds her at arm's length.

MUM   But Elaine – you just got to start getting on with it.

ELAINE   I don't know how. I don't know how!

ELAINE and MUM exit.

SCENE THREE

In the house. MUM is alone. There's a knock on the door.
MCNAMARA enters, carrying a tray of beautifully-presented
vegetables, fruits and flowers.

MUM	Oh, Mr McNamara.
McNAMARA	I hope I'm not disturbing you.
MUM	Not at all. Please come in.
McNAMARA	I brought you some veg from the allotment …
MUM	For us?
McNAMARA	… and some flowers from my garden.
MUM	Oh, you shouldn't have.
McNAMARA	I thought I should tell you … I saw Elaine up at the allotment this morning.

ELAINE enters. She recoils when she sees MCNAMARA.

ELAINE	What you doing here? What's he doing here?
MUM	Calm down, love. It's only Mr McNamara. He's brought some

veg for us. Look. Look at this
beautiful tomato.

ELAINE   It's poison!

MUM   Oh, Elaine.

ELAINE   He's spit on it. He's put a spell on
it. It's poison. Don't touch it! I
wouldn't eat it if I was dying of
hunger! It's puke! Yuk! You
should see his allotment. It's a
disgrace! What's he doing
here?

MUM   Elaine, Mr McNamara says he's
seen you out and about when you
should be at school. He's seen
you in your dad's allotment.

ELAINE   Spy! Spy! He's always staring,
watching with his evil eye. He
thought Dad was stupid and
messy and … And he thinks I am
as well. Always did, right from
when I was a little girl.

MUM   Take no notice, Mr McNamara.

ELAINE   Mum!

MUM   It's because he's worried
about you. Because he cares for
us!

McNAMARA	I've always been concerned about you, Elaine.
ELAINE	Mum! Can you not see?
MUM	I'm sorry, Mr McNamara.
ELAINE	I'm not! I'm not!
McNAMARA	I understand. It's so difficult. A spirit like hers, and no man in the house ...
ELAINE	What? Mum?
MUM	Why don't you leave us, Mr McNamara? I'll calm her down.

McNAMARA exits. MUM turns angrily to ELAINE.

MUM	Now, then, madam ...

SCENE FOUR

Elaine is in the allotment. She keeps reaching to the earth, pushing undergrowth aside, searching.

ELAINE   No fairy. No fairy. No fairy.
No fairy. Daddy! Daddy! Daddy!

She catches a seed in mid-air. She spits at it.

ELAINE   Grow like mushroom, grow like
magic, grow like happiness in the
heart.

She spits at it again, plants it in the earth, puts horse muck on it.
She blinks her eyes fast.

ELAINE   Grow like mushroom. Grow like
magic. Grow like happiness in the
heart. One two three four five six
seven eight ... Daddy!

McNamara enters, watches from his own allotment.
Elaine looks around, sees him. She catches a spider.

ELAINE   Spider! Big fat spider.
You can make spells with spiders.
Spider spider spin your web,
Spider spin around my head
Spider spider sit dead still

Spider work my wicked will.
Kill McNamara! Ah!

ELAINE puts the spider down. She turns to MCNAMARA again.
He continues to watch in silence.
ELAINE spits in despair. She sits on the earth. She takes out paper and pencil from her canvas bag, begins to draw. She takes out her seedhead. She sings and rattles to herself, rocks back and forward.
The WILD BOY comes out from the wilderness. He watches her. He weirdly joins in with her song.

ELAINE   Oh!

WILD BOY reaches out towards ELAINE.

ELAINE   Don't you dare! Who are you?

They circle each other. Larks sing high above.
The WILD BOY indicates them with his hands – a gesture of great tenderness.

ELAINE   Skylarks. Yes, they're beautiful.

WILD BOY sings weirdly again – a discordant imitation of lark song.

ELAINE   Who are you? Are you wagging it
                 as well? Which school you at?

WILD BOY discordantly imitates ELAINE'S voice.

ELAINE   You can't talk! That's all right. I can't write. They call me stupid for it, but I'm not. I'm not!

She reaches out, touches his hands.

ELAINE   Fur. What are you? I can draw, though. Look. I'll draw you.

She draws WILD BOY.

ELAINE   Look. This is you. This is … What's your name? I'll call you … Wild Boy. I can't write it.

She makes a few scribbles to indicate his name.

ELAINE   There. Best I can do. Ha. And here's my name. Elaine. I can just do that. That's who I am. Say my name, Elaine. E-laine.

WILD BOY weirdly imitates her.
Suddenly, ELAINE remembers MCNAMARA.

ELAINE   Quick! Get back in the weeds where he can't see you.

WILD BOY doesn't go back.
MCNAMARA shakes his head, sighs.

McNAMARA	Silly girl. Stop talking to thin air. Pull yourself together. Get out of there. Get back to school before your mother loses her wits.

He continues to shake his head and to sigh as he watches.

ELAINE	He hasn't seen you. Say my name. E-laine.
WILD BOY	E-ay.
ELAINE	Elaine.
WILD BOY	E-ay.
ELAINE	That's right! That's nearly right! Oh, Wild Boy! Draw me. Go on. It's your turn. You draw me.

She pushes the pencil and paper into his hands.
He inspects them, confused.

ELAINE	Just draw what you see.

He moves the pencil across the paper.

ELAINE	Is this what you see? Is this really what you see? Oh, Wild Boy! Are you a fairy? Did you grow from the fairy seed I planted with my dad ninety-nine weeks ago?

ELAINE gently touches him, inspects him.

ELAINE   No wings. Heavy. Fur on your
hands and feet. You're … ugly.
No, not ugly. Come with me.
Come on. Come on.

ELAINE tugs his hand. He holds back, glances towards McNAMARA.

ELAINE   Just take no notice of him. He
doesn't see you, does he? He
doesn't see!
Come on, quick! Come with me.
Oh, come on, Wild Boy. Let's go
home!

They leave the allotment together. The lark song intensifies.
WILD BOY gazes up to the larks, gestures towards them again, imitates their song.
ELAINE laughs joyfully, tugs at him, and they hurry away.

SCENE FIVE

THE CHORUS OF VOICES

The voices commentate on ELAINE'S return home from the allotment.

> – Did you see?
>
> – Eh?
>
> – That lass. That Elaine.
>
> – Her again.
>
> – Aye. Did you see her coming down from the allotments?
>
> – Talking to thin air.
>
> – Laughing at thin air.
>
> – Singing at thin air.
>
> – Babbling and laughing like a daft thing, she was.
>
> – Babbling and laughing and pointing at the larks in the sky.
>
> – Too much sun, mebbe.
>
> – It has been blazing hot.
>
> – They put you away for that, you know.

– They don't.

– They do.

– Put you away and chuck away the key.

– They'll come and get her, eh?

– Aye. A big white van and big strong nurses.

– Come on, Elaine, they'll say.

– Come on, love, we'll not harm you.

– This won't hurt a bit.

– Poor soul.

– Aye, poor soul.

– Hee hee hee.

– Wouldn't want her playing with my kids.

– Me neither.

– Not safe, letting her run round like that.

– Shouldn't be allowed.

– Lets the estate down.

– Lock her up, that's what I say.

– Aye. Take her away. Lock her up.

– Lock her up!

SCENE SIX

The kitchen. MUM is there.
ELAINE and WILD BOY enter.

MUM	Where you been, girl? The school's been on again. You've been wagging it again. What am I going to do with you? Oh, Elaine.
ELAINE	I went to the allotment. I found …
MUM	That place again. Why's nobody taken it over yet? Elaine, all it'll do is make you worse.
ELAINE	I found …

ELAINE gestures towards WILD BOY, showing him to MUM.
MUM sees nothing.

MUM	I talked to the school. I talked to the doctors.
ELAINE	The doctors!
MUM	They want to look at you, Elaine. They want to see …

33

ELAINE   See what?

MUM   See what's wrong. See if there's
             anything they can do ...

ELAINE holds WILD BOY in front of her mum.
WILD BOY smiles tenderly into MUM'S eyes.
ELAINE realises that MUM sees nothing.

ELAINE   Look, Mum. Look. Oh, Wild
             Boy, she can't see you. She can't
             see!

MUM moves close to ELAINE, peers into her eyes.

MUM   Elaine, what's going on in there?
             What's happened to my little girl?

SCENE SEVEN

ELAINE'S bedroom. Night. The moon shines in through the window.
ELAINE is at the table. WILD BOY sits on the table.

ELAINE   Larks soar against the sun by day,
                        bats flicker flack against the moon
                        by night. You see them, Wild
                        Boy? Flicker flack, wild wings in
                        the night.
                        Say my name. Elaine. E-laine.

WILD BOY   E-ay.

ELAINE shows him a drawing of the moon, then points at the window and the moon.

ELAINE   That's the moon, Wild Boy.
                        That's the moon that lights the
                        night and pulls the seas and drives
                        us wild. Moooon.

WILD BOY   Oooooo!

ELAINE shakes the seedhead. She starts to dance and yell and sing.
She draws WILD BOY into the dance. He weirdly sings and yells along with her.

ELAINE   Dance, my wild boy. Dance!

MUM (*from outside the room*)
                Elaine! Elaine!

They continue to dance and yell. MUM *enters.*

MUM	What's going on in here?
ELAINE	Just dancing, Mum.
MUM	You'll bring the house down. You'll …
ELAINE	I'll what.
MUM	You'll drive me wild.

MUM *looks around the room. She does not see* WILD BOY, *but she appears to feel that something is wrong.* WILD BOY *moves close to her, peers closely at her.*

ELAINE	What do you see, Mum?
MUM	What do you mean? Nothing. Your room. What's that …?
ELAINE	That what?
MUM	That … smell or something. No, not a smell.

MUM *moves closer to* WILD BOY. *She sniffs, narrows her eyes.*

ELAINE	Look closer, Mum. Closer.

MUM	What did you do today, at the allotment?
ELAINE	Just mooched. Just dreamed. Just remembered.
MUM	No fairies?
ELAINE	No fairies.
MUM	I love you. You know that, don't you?
ELAINE	Yes.
MUM	You're such a brave girl.
ELAINE	No, I'm not.
MUM	When the doctors look at you ...
ELAINE	They'll see nothing.
MUM	It's because they want to see what they can do for you.
ELAINE	They'll do nothing.
MUM	It's because I love you, love.
ELAINE	I know that. Look closely, Mum. Please. Look with your ... inside eye.
MUM	Inside eye. Oh, Elaine, what nonsense is that? I'm looking closely at my lovely girl.

ELAINE   Look closer. See what you can
                   see.

MUM kisses her cheek, hugs her.

MUM   Oh, Elaine. It's so hard for you.
                   Even harder than it is for me. But
                   things'll get better, my little love.
                   Sleep tight. Sweet dreams.

MUM exits.

ELAINE   She doesn't see. She doesn't see
                   you, Wild Boy …

SCENE EIGHT

A doctor's surgery. On the wall are diagrams of the eye and the brain, and an eye-test chart.
The DOCTOR *and* ELAINE *face each other.*
MUM watches nervously.
WILD BOY stands apart, watching, then begins to move through the room, inspecting it.

DOCTOR	Look at the letters, Elaine. Tell me which ones you can see.
ELAINE	One that's like a tree and one that's like a tent and a moon and a half a moon and they slither and slide …
MUM	She can't read, Doctor. Not a single word.
DOCTOR	We all have our cross to—
ELAINE	It's not a cross.
DOCTOR	I'd like you to look at these now.

The DOCTOR *shows* ELAINE *a series of cards containing blots and blotches.*

DOCTOR	Just say what you see, Elaine. Don't worry. Nobody's trying to catch you out. Just say what you see. Come on, try to take part.

39

MUM	D'you realise what this is costing, Elaine?
ELAINE	I see a larkybird's heart thumping in the dark. I see the onions run to seed. I see me mum's tongue flapping and flipping when she whispers I was such a lovely girl. I see me dad …
DOCTOR	What?
MUM	Your dad what?
ELAINE	I see him planting fairies in the garden.
DOCTOR	Fairies?
MUM	She's turning back into a baby, Doctor. Her dad was lovely, but some of the things he told her …
ELAINE	Fairies. He's got spit and horse muck on his hands. We count to ninety-nine … Wild Boy! We grew a wild boy, not a fairy!
DOCTOR	A wild boy?
ELAINE	A wild boy!

She looks at WILD BOY and laughs.

DOCTOR   What are you looking at now,
             Elaine? What are you seeing
             now?

*The DOCTOR goes to ELAINE with an eye torch in his
hand.*
She recoils but he holds her. He shines it into her eye.

DOCTOR   Just stay calm, Elaine. I need to
             look inside, deep inside.

ELAINE   What you looking at? Get off!
             Get off!

*WILD BOY moves to the DOCTOR'S back. He pulls the
DOCTOR'S hand away from ELAINE.*
The DOCTOR is alarmed, amazed, uncomprehending.
ELAINE goes to WILD BOY. They hold hands and laugh.
They begin to dance and sing.
*The DOCTOR pulls himself together, takes a notebook
from his pocket, begins to write as he watches ELAINE'S
antics. She giggles at him, then plucks a spider from the
air before her face.*

ELAINE   Spider!
             Spider spider spin your web
             Spider spin into my head
             Spider spider sit dead still
             Spider work my wicked will.
             Doctor, be gone!

She giggles, seeing that nothing happens to the DOCTOR.

41

ELAINE Ah, well, it doesn't always work.
Pretty spider.

She runs to the eye-test chart, points to the letters.

ELAINE That's E for Elaine. That's D for
Dad. That's M for Mum. That's
W for Wild Boy. See!
Dance, Wild Boy, dance!

ELAINE dances, yells and sings with WILD BOY.
The DOCTOR gives up writing, goes to MUM.

MUM Stop it, Elaine! You'll …

ELAINE I know I will. Dance, Wild Boy,
dance! Dance and yell.
Yell that hard we'll wake the
dead!

ELAINE and WILD BOY run off, leaving the DOCTOR and
MUM disturbed and bemused.

SCENE NINE

Elaine's bedroom. Night. The moon shines through the window.
WILD BOY is on the bed, staring at the moon.
ELAINE crouches with her ear to the floor, listening.

ELAINE	McNamara. He's been here for hours downstairs with Mum.
WILD BOY	Oooooo.
ELAINE	That's right. Moon. Mooooon.
WILD BOY	Moooon.
ELAINE	Yes! E-laine.
WILD BOY	E-laine.
ELAINE	Yes! Yes! You can talk! What's your name?
WILD BOY	E-laine.
ELAINE	No. That's my name.
WILD BOY	E-laine?
ELAINE	No. Your name. Never mind. Where did you come from? You understand? Where did you come from? Draw it!

WILD BOY draws. He now has more control over the
pencil.
He passes what he has drawn to ELAINE.

ELAINE   That's me, isn't it? But draw me
                               other things.

WILD BOY draws again. As he draws, he looks around
him, as if seeing things that ELAINE cannot see.

ELAINE   What are these, Wild Boy?
                               Where do you see these?

WILD BOY points into the spaces around them.
He tries to show her what he sees.

ELAINE   Here? Now? I see nothing.

WILD BOY laughs and murmurs, as if communicating
with another.
He puts down the paper and pencils and begins to dance,
as if with another.
ELAINE watches in fascination and frustration.

ELAINE   Who you dancing with, Wild
                               Boy? Oh, if I could see through
                               your eyes.

McNAMARA (*from outside***)**
                               Elaine! Elaine Grew!

ELAINE   McNamara!

44

McNAMARA comes in, switches the light on.

ELAINE MUM!

McNAMARA Your mum will see you later. She told me about your performance today in the doctor's.

He picks up the scattered drawings. He paces the room looking about him.
WILD BOY follows him closely, watches him closely.

McNAMARA You have to learn the ways of the world, girl.

ELAINE What are you doing here?

McNAMARA You have to knuckle down. You have to control yourself.

ELAINE You're nothing to do with me!

McNAMARA These things, for instance. They're like products of a twisted mind.

ELAINE Spider spider spin your web Spider spin around my head ...

WILD BOY moves closer to McNAMARA, holds his face close to his.

McNAMARA What's that ... smell or something?

45

ELAINE	Spider spider sit dead still Spider work my wicked will …
McNAMARA	I saw you, as a little girl, wriggling through the grass, crawling through the weeds, slithering through the mud. I heard him, urging you on.
ELAINE	Kill McNamara!
McNAMARA	She'll grow up wrong, I used to say. You got to train kids proper, just like plants. You got to stake them and prune them and shape them. Otherwise … She's growing up wrong, I used to say. And after all these years, you've growed up wrong, Elaine Grew. Growed up wrong, like a plant gone wild. You need training …

He crumples the drawings, breaks pencils, takes up the seedhead and discards it again.
WILD BOY'S stance becomes more sinister, more threatening.

McNAMARA	Put away the things of childhood, Elaine Grew.
ELAINE	Kill McNamara. Kill!

McNAMARA	Crawl back out of the wilderness.
ELAINE	Kill McNamara! Kill!
McNAMARA	Come into the real world. What's that … smell or something?
ELAINE	Spider spider spin your web …

WILD BOY's face is almost touching McNAMARA's.

McNAMARA	What's that … something. Agh, something!
ELAINE	Spider spin around my head …
McNAMARA	What d'you get up to here, in the darkness, on your own?
ELAINE	Spider spider sit dead still …
McNAMARA	One day, maybe soon …
ELAINE	Spider work my wicked will.
McNAMARA	… I will take your father's part.
ELAINE	Kill McNamara. Kill!
McNAMARA	One day, maybe very soon.
ELAINE	Shut him up!

WILD BOY clamps his hand across McNAMARA's mouth.
McNAMARA recoils in shock, then retreats slowly.
WILD BOY follows, as if herding McNAMARA out.

47

McNAMARA   What do you get up to, in here,
                  in the dark, in the light of the
                  moon? What's that ... something?
                  Wild girl. Wild girl. We'll have to
                  tame you.

McNAMARA exits.
WILD BOY dances in triumph.
ELAINE burns with anger.

ELAINE   Moooooon!

WILD BOY   Ooooooooooo!

SCENE TEN

Elaine's bedroom. Later the same night.
ELAINE and WILD BOY crouch on her bed, bathed in moonlight.
ELAINE has been cutting paper into the shapes of letters.
She holds up letters in random patterns.
WILD BOY watches, as if determined to listen and learn.

ELAINE
I've made a word out of letters.
It's a name, your name. Don't
know what it says, but when I say
it I say Skoosh. Skoosh!
Lovely sound, lovely word, lovely
name.
Where do sounds and words and
names come from? From deep in
the deep in the deep of your
heart.
Where do letters come from?
From a table top, from the point
of a pen, from the pictures
running round the walls.
How do you make the noises
from inside your heart match up
with letters in the world?
I don't know. I'll call you Skoosh.

She holds the letters before her mouth as she speaks the word.

49

She throws the letters into the air and lets them scatter.
WILD BOY laughs and plays at catching the letters.

ELAINE   How does it happen? How do you make the letters catch the word? How do you make the sound catch the letters? I can't do it, but I make the sound. Skoosh. The letters don't matter. Skoosh! Skoosh!

MUM enters. She stands in the doorway, watching.

ELAINE   What is your name?

WILD BOY   Skoosh.

ELAINE   What is my name?

WILD BOY   Elaine.

ELAINE   See? Hear? I taught him how to talk.

MUM   I'm keeping you in, my girl!

ELAINE   Mum!

MUM   I'm at the end of my tether. What can I do? I'm locking you in.

MUM exits, closing the door.
ELAINE rushes to the door, finds it locked.
She rattles the window.

ELAINE	Door locked. Window locked. Let me out! No way out, my Wild Boy Skoosh.
WILD BOY	Skoosh.
ELAINE	Hahaha. Skoosh!
WILD BOY	Mooooon!
ELAINE	Mooooooon! Skoosh! Listen. We'll make a wilderness here in my room. We'll make a garden where we can crawl like lizards, like snakes, where we can slither deep into the wild.
WILD BOY	Wiiiiild!
ELAINE	Yes, Wild Boy. Now, what do we need? Soil, plants, sunlight, rain. Useless.

*ELAINE **runs to the door and the window, rattles them.***

ELAINE	Let me out!
WILD BOY (*trying to imitate Elaine*)	E eee ou! E ee ou!
ELAINE	Shh. No. Listen, Wild Boy Skoosh. My dad … Yes, my dad. You

51

don't know my dad but he was wonderful. My dad said that the greatest of all gardens is the mind. He said in the mind you can grow anything. Anything!

WILD BOY E-y-ing.

ELAINE Anything, that's right. We can dream a garden. We can imagine a garden. Dream it, Wild Boy. Close your eyes and watch it grow.

ELAINE closes her eyes, dreams and imagines.
WILD BOY copies her, keeps glancing at her to check that he's imagining properly.

ELAINE You have to see the onions and raspberries and leeks and the flowers, and you have to feel the soil in your fingers and under your feet and you have to feel where the edge of the wilderness is ...

WILD BOY I-er-ess.

ELAINE That's right. Wilderness! Can you see it and feel it, Wild Boy Skoosh? Can you smell the soil

and the scents of the flowers and
feel the sun on you and the
breeze and … Can you see
anything, Skoosh?

*WILD BOY is becoming distracted. He looks away from
ELAINE, towards the moonlight pouring through the
window, towards the outside world.*
*ELAINE opens her eyes, calls to him. But he has grown
lethargic.*

ELAINE   Skoosh!

WILD BOY (*half-heartedly*)
                   Skoosh!

ELAINE   Look, this is the earth and these
                   are raspberries and this is a
                   chrysanthemum and this is the
                   edge of the … Let me out!

WILD BOY   E ee ou!

ELAINE   Mum!

WILD BOY   U!

ELAINE   Let me out!

MUM (*from outside*)
                   Elaine! Elaine, just calm down,
                   love!

ELAINE   Let me out!

53

MUM (*from outside*)

>   Oh, Elaine. Be a good girl, will
>   you?

ELAINE   Let me out! Let me out!

*WILD BOY clambers on to the bed. He lies there,
dispirited.*
ELAINE becomes more desperate, more yearning.

ELAINE   Oh, isn't it lovely here, Skoosh?
>   The sun, the air. Can you hear
>   those lovely lovely larkybirds?
>   Look, Wild Boy Skoosh. This is
>   the edge of the wilderness – the
>   long grass, the high weeds. I'll
>   crawl in there, like a little lizard,
>   like a little snake.

*ELAINE crawls, as if she's in the wilderness of the
allotment, shouldering aside weeds and grasses. There is
lark song.*

ELAINE   Crawl crawl. Seeds in me eyes
>   and nose, soil on me hands and
>   knees.
>   Oh, look: here's a lark come
>   down!

The song of the lark brings a change.
The bedroom and the allotment merge once more.
WILD BOY exits. DAD enters, whistling softly.

DAD   Go on, little one. Crawl deep
                           into the wilderness. Go on. Get
                           lost in there. Go on. I'll be here.
                           Just call out if you get lost and I'll
                           bring you back to me.

ELAINE   Daddy!

ELAINE doesn't look back.

DAD   Elaine! Elaine! Wild girl! Time to
                           come back out.

MUM (*from outside*)
                           Elaine! Elaine!

DAD exits. MUM comes into the room.

MUM   Elaine! Elaine! What you doing?
                           Elaine.
                           What you doing on the floor?
                           Who you been talking to?

ELAINE   Mum. Is he still there?

ELAINE doesn't look back.

MUM   Who? Who?

ELAINE   Oh, Mum, look closely.

MUM   Oh, Elaine, there's nothing.
                           There's nobody.

55

ELAINE	Can you at least see the long grass and the raspberries and hear the larkybirds singing singing …?
MUM	Oh, my little love.

ELAINE turns and looks.

ELAINE	There's nobody. There's not even Skoosh now.
MUM	Oh, Elaine.

ELAINE crouches on the floor, stares into the empty room.

ELAINE	Skoosh! Skooooooosh!

SCENE ELEVEN

THE CHORUS OF VOICES

– She's crackers, of course.

– Really crackers. Right round the twist.

– Have you heard her? Howling and yowling.

– Chanting and ranting.

– Making a noise fit to wake the dead.

– If you're lucky you'll see her.

– See her?

– Aye. Just watch the window.

– See her dancing like a loony.

– See her banging on the windows.

– Hear her yelling, Let me out!

– Let me out!

– Let me out!

– Her mum must be at the end of her tether, eh?

– Aye. Poor soul.

– Poor soul.

– Thank God she's locked her in.

– Aye. And let's hope she's chucked the key away.

– Don't want something like that running round the place.

– Little wild thing howling and yowling.

– Little monster chanting and ranting.

– Little devil doing …

– Just imagine what she could do.

– Such awful things.

– Here! We got kids of our own out here, you know!

– Keep that wild thing under lock and key!

– We got kids to keep safe out here!

– Just imagine, if she got hold of a child of yours.

– Aye.

– Aye …

– Just imagine, if she was a child of yours.

– No.

– No …

– Don't bear thinking of.

SCENE TWELVE

The doctor's surgery. ELAINE is dejected, exhausted. She sits opposite the DOCTOR.
MUM stands nervously watching.

DOCTOR	And what did this wild boy look like, Elaine?
MUM	Come on, love. Please join in.
ELAINE	This tall. Arms and legs, just like us. A head, just like us. He was just like us.

ELAINE looks around the room, as if seeking WILD BOY.

ELAINE	I keep thinking he'll come back. But I think he went back to the allotment.
DOCTOR	And what else, Elaine? Did he have wings or anything like that?
ELAINE	Wings? Don't be daft.
DOCTOR	A tail, maybe?
ELAINE	Are you joking?
DOCTOR	OK. So what was it that made him ... wild?
ELAINE	He came out of the wilderness ...

DOCTOR   The wilderness?

MUM   Her dad's allotment, Doctor. It
                was always such a mess.

ELAINE   It wasn't a mess. It was beautiful!
                He couldn't talk …
                I taught him how to talk. So I
                can't be that stupid, can I?

MUM   Of course you're not stupid, love.

ELAINE   And he could sing like the larks.
                And there was fur on his hands
                and feet.

DOCTOR   Fur, Elaine?

ELAINE   Fur. Yes, fur.

DOCTOR   Ah. And … the kind of fur? Like
                a cat, maybe, or a bear, or …
                What else has fur? Like a fluffy
                toy, perhaps.

ELAINE   See, you don't believe me.
                Nobody'll ever believe me.

MUM   But, love, you've got to see, it's
                so …

ELAINE   Dad would have. Dad would have
                believed.
                Dad would have seen him as well!
                Wild Boy! Skoosh! Where are
                you?

SCENE THIRTEEN

Elaine's bedroom. Daytime. ELAINE is crawling on the floor, as if in the allotment.
MUM and MCNAMARA stand watching.
ELAINE is absorbed in her own actions and doesn't see them there.

ELAINE   I'll grow him again. That's what I'll do. I'll grow him again.

She catches a fairy seed, spits on it, plants it.

ELAINE   Fairy seed. Horse muck. Spit. In the ground.
One two three four five six seven ...
No fairy. No Wild Boy.

She crawls again.

ELAINE   Crawl deeper, Elaine. Crawl like a lizard, crawl like a snake.

MUM   They said it's grief. They said it's just her age. They said to keep an eye on her. They said she might just start getting better. But they said if she doesn't ...

McNAMARA   What can I do? Elaine. Elaine!

MCNAMARA moves towards ELAINE, but MUM holds him back.

ELAINE plucks a spider from the earth.

ELAINE	Spider spider spin your web.
MUM	She gets so lost in her own world.
ELAINE	Spider spin around my head.
MUM	Can't hear, can't see.
ELAINE	Spider spider sit dead still.
McNAMARA	Elaine. Elaine!
ELAINE	Spider bring me what I will. Wild Boy. Wild Boy!
MUM	Elaine. Elaine! Where are you?
ELAINE	Horse muck. Spit. Grow like mushroom, grow like magic. One two three four five …
MUM	Elaine! Elaine!

ELAINE looks up, sees MUM there.

ELAINE	Mum! Fancy seeing you here. Isn't it lovely? Come on in.
MUM	What, love?
ELAINE	Come on in.

MUM   Oh, Elaine!

MUM looks at MCNAMARA. She wants to join in with her daughter, but the man's presence inhibits her, embarrasses her.

ELAINE   Come on, Mum. Please join in.
Crawl like a lizard, crawl like a snake.
Crawl deep into the wilderness.

MUM   Oh, Elaine.

ELAINE   Oh, Mum. It's what Dad would have said.

MUM sighs, glances at MCNAMARA, then joins ELAINE in the imaginary allotment.
She crawls beside ELAINE.

MUM   Where are we, love?

ELAINE   We're at the allotment, Mum.
Look, the grass, the weeds, the sun shining down, the larkybirds singing.

MUM looks around the room.

MUM   We're in your bedroom, love.

ELAINE   Can you not see, can you not hear, can you not smell?

MUM	Yes, love.
ELAINE	Good. We might find a fairy in here, you know.
MUM	A fairy?
ELAINE	Yes, a real fairy. You can grow them, you know.
MUM	Really? Oh, love. Give me a cuddle, love.

MUM and ELAINE hug each other.

ELAINE	You don't believe me, do you?
MUM	I do.
ELAINE	You can't see anything, can you?
MUM	Yes, I can.
ELAINE	Come with me to the allotment.
MUM	Oh, Elaine.
ELAINE	You've never been, have you, not since … You used to come. Do you remember? Do you remember how we used to dance there, all of us together?

ELAINE tugs her mum's hand. She yearns to leave the house and take her mother with her, but MUM holds back, undecided.

McNAMARA

You'll mess her up even worse.
You'll mess yourself up.

MUM looks at him, listens to him, holds ELAINE.

McNAMARA

Give her rules and regulations.
Discipline her. Tame her. It's like
gardening. How d'you get the
best plants? Proper feeding,
proper watering, proper pruning.
Start growing the wrong way and
you pull them back. Start getting
wild and you cut them back. You
show them what's the right way
and what's the wrong way to
grow. You train them, and you
keep on training them, otherwise
there's just ... wilderness.

ELAINE

Come with me, Mum.

MUM smiles, turns away from McNAMARA, and hurries off with ELAINE.
McNAMARA shakes his head, sighs, slowly follows.

SCENE FOURTEEN

THE CHORUS OF VOICES

They commentate on the journey out of the estate.

– Did you see them?

– Who?

– Daft Elaine Grew and her mother, man.

– The crazy one?

– Aye. Did you see them walking out the estate? Running up the hill to the allotments?

– Weirdos, eh?

– The kid pulling her mum. That bloke McNamara following them.

– They looked wild, eh?

– Wild. Wild.

– The mother looked as crackers as the kid, eh?

– It happens like that with families. One of them starts cracking up and before you know it they're all belting round the twist.

– Climbing up the pole.

– Poor souls.

– Aye. Hee hee hee. Poor souls.

– Mebbe they were chasing fairies.

– Or running after things that weren't there.

– Hey, Elaine, bring us a fairy back!

– Did you hear, though?

– Eh?

– Did you hear the birds?

– The birds?

– Aye. Did you hear the way they were singing?

– Now you mention it …

– Never heard them that loud.

– And never seen that many.

– Like the sky was filled with larkybirds way up high.

– And the sun that bright and everything that still.

– Weird.

– Aye. Weird.

SCENE FIFTEEN

The allotment. MUM and ELAINE enter.
MUM looks around her in wonder, touches the earth, the plants, smells the air, feels the sun on her face, listens to the larks that sing high above.
Her whole body relaxes.
She smiles with ELAINE, and joyful memories move through her.
ELAINE laughs and draws her MUM into the weeds and long grasses. Her MUM joins in.

ELAINE   That's right, Mum. Seeds in your eyes and nose, soil on your hands and knees. Crawl in deeper, deeper. Come on. We might find a fairy in here, you know.

MUM   Might we? A real fairy?

ELAINE   A real fairy.

MUM   Oh, love.

ELAINE   Come on, Mum.
You can grow them, you know, like they was leeks or raspberries. Dad showed me ... Yes, Dad. Look, here's a fairy seed!

ELAINE plucks a fairy seed from the air.

ELAINE   Spit and horse muck.

She spits on the seed, plants it, throws horse muck on to it.

ELAINE   Then the spell:
                   Come along, my little fairy, grow
                   like mushroom …
                   Come on, Mum. Join in. Say it
                   along with me.

MUM is shy at first, but then joins in more confidently.

MUM/ELAINE (*together*)
                   Grow like mushroom, grow like
                   magic,
                   grow like happiness in the heart.

ELAINE   Come on, Mum.

MUM/ELAINE
                   Grow like mushroom, grow like
                   magic, grow like happiness in the
                   heart.

ELAINE   Now spit on it again.

MUM   Elaine!

MUM giggles and recoils.

ELAINE   Go on. Spit on it.

MUM spits half-heartedly.

70

ELAINE   Properly!

MUM   I can't!

ELAINE   Yes, you can.

ELAINE demonstrates how to spit properly.
MUM copies her, laughing.

ELAINE   Now blink dead fast ninety-nine
                        times.

MUM blinks fast.

MUM   Like this?

ELAINE   Yes, like this.

They blink and count and laugh together and end in
giggles. Then they gaze down at the fairy seed.

ELAINE   Ah, well. Mebbe this one's a
                        ninety-nine yearer.

MUM   A ninety-nine yearer!

ELAINE   Isn't it lovely here, Mum?

MUM   Yes ...
                        Remember how we used to
                        dance here?

ELAINE   Yes.

MUM   Give us a cuddle, love.

71

The larks sing. MUM and ELAINE hug each other.
WILD BOY emerges from the wilderness. He watches
them.
MUM sees him over ELAINE'S shoulder.

MUM   Oh!

ELAINE   Mum?

ELAINE turns and sees WILD BOY.

ELAINE   Didn't I tell you? Oh, Wild Boy, I
                     thought you'd gone.

MUM   Wild Boy.

WILD BOY   I oy.

WILD BOY moves towards them.
MUM reaches out and touches his hands.

MUM   Fur! What are you?

ELAINE   It's my Wild Boy, Mum. It's
                     Skoosh. What's my name?

WILD BOY   E-laine.

ELAINE   What's your name?

WILD BOY   Skoosh!

MUM   What's my name?

WILD BOY regards her with great tenderness.

MUM   What's my name?

WILD BOY   M-um.

ELAINE   Oh, Wild Boy!

MUM, ELAINE and WILD BOY begin to dance.

ELAINE   Come on, Mum. Come on, Wild
                     Boy. Let's wake the dead!

They dance and sing, then become still.
ELAINE reaches down into the grass, picks up an eggshell.

ELAINE   Here's a lark's egg, Mum.
                     See, speckled white outside,
                     brilliant white inside. A little lark
                     grew out of this. From yellow
                     yolk and salty white and flew
                     away. A miracle.

MUM   A miracle. You were once a yolky
                     little salty thing.
                     And look at you now, so lovely.

MUM and ELAINE are absorbed by their memories and by
the miracle of the eggshell.
WILD BOY exits.
DAD enters, whistling softly. He stands watching his wife
and daughter.
Lark song.

ELAINE   Oh! Here's a lark come down.

MUM and ELAINE are very still. They do not turn.

DAD	Go on. Go on. Crawl deep into the wilderness. Just call out if you get lost. Grow like mushroom, grow like magic, grow like happiness in the heart. Spider, spider, spin your web. Wild girls. Wild girls!

DAD watches.
MUM and ELAINE remain very still. The larks sing.

ELAINE	I love you, Mum.
MUM	I love you.

DAD exits.
MCNAMARA enters, carrying raspberries in his hands.
MUM turns.

MUM	Mr McNamara.

MCNAMARA is confused, uncertain.

McNAMARA	The larks are so loud today.
MUM	Were you watching us?
McNAMARA	I tried. I couldn't see. You were in the wilderness. I saw …

MUM	What?
ELAINE	What?
McNAMARA	The larks so loud. The sun so bright … I brought you these.
MUM	Raspberries.
McNAMARA	They were hanging over my allotment. I reached deep into the thorns.
ELAINE	Dad's.
McNAMARA	Yes, your dad's. They're … delicious. Sweeter than any I ever grew.

MUM takes the raspberries from him. She hands one to ELAINE.
McNAMARA exits.
MUM and ELAINE eat the raspberries.

MUM	Delicious.
ELAINE	Raspberries. Delicious and sweet and wild.

They laugh at the juice and the stains.
WILD BOY comes out from the wilderness. He moves around them, but they are so absorbed in each other and in their memories that they do not see him at first.

Then they smile together, seeing that he is there.
He gestures for them to explore the allotment and its wilderness.

ELAINE   Come on, Mum.

ELAINE and MUM move into the wilderness.
WILD BOY dances, then follows them.

(END)

AFTERWORD

We lived in a small estate on a steep hill in a small Tyneside town. The centre was just below us: the square with trees and benches, the Co-op, The Blue Bell, The Jubilee. There was a lovely clutter of buildings and names: *Dragone's Cafe*; MAYS' FASHION'S; **Howes Junk**; SPEED THE PLOUGH TAVERN; *Le Palais de Dans*. Churches and working men's clubs, busy streets, long queues at bus stops, a steep high street of pork shops and bakers and fishmongers leading down to our railway station. Then were the warehouses and factories, then much further down was the Tyne, and then Newcastle, packed densely on the opposite bank.

Higher up, above our estate, came emptiness, space and light. I remember bright breezy days, leaving the house, leaving the estate, crossing Rectory Road, walking upwards to the playing fields, then the heather hills at the summit of the town. There was a freedom in walking away from the centre, in climbing closer to the massive lark-filled sky.

The allotments were just before the playing fields, squeezed into the space between the houses of Fleming Gardens and Windy Ridge. My grandfather's was the third one up, behind the pointed timber fence. You put your hand through the timbers to unlatch the gate, then stepped on to the cinder path that led past the leek trenches, the chrysanthemums and the cold frames to the greenhouse.

Usually he was waiting there, sitting on a seat of old bricks, gazing out across the fields, puffing on his pipe.

'Aye,' he'd say, turning to acknowledge me, wiping his hand across the grin that had flickered on his face. 'Aye, aye.' And he'd spit, wipe his grin again and turn his face to the fields again.

He was a man with little small talk, with no apparent desire to teach me anything with words. No matter what the season, he wore a dark serge suit, a tightly-fastened waistcoat, white shirt, dark tie, checked cloth cap, and black Oxford boots.

We shared long easy silences, long hours of doing nothing very much. We pottered in the breathless greenhouse and the breezy garden. We lit smouldering smoky fires of weeds. He held me up as I plunged a watering can into the great rainwater butt and watched the great glug and gush and suck the water made around my hand. We watered leeks and onions. We clipped chrysanthemums and plucked sweet warm tomatoes and wrapped them in Daily Mirrors. We swigged from huge bottles of lemonade. He lifted his cap, wiped the sweat from his head, replaced the cap again. He tugged at his tight collar. He puffed on his pipe. He spat from one side of his mouth while holding the pipe clenched in the other. He grinned wryly at me. He said, 'Aye' and 'Aye, aye.' He took his watch from his waistcoat pocket and raised his eyes and shook his head at the passing of the day.

If we went back to that time now and leaned on the allotment fence and watched the old man and the boy in there, it might all seem pretty pleasant, pretty aimless, pretty pointless. In some obscure way, though, the boy in there was preparing to be a writer.

Years later I was approached by Sally Goldsworthy, Head of Education at the Lyric Theatre Hammersmith. Would I be interested in writing a play to be included in the theatre's remarkable programme of work for children? I pondered the idea. I sat at my desk before a computer beneath a reading lamp. I contemplated an empty space, a stage, and the memories and sensations of the allotment rushed to fill it.

The smells of turned earth and pipe smoke, onions and leeks and chrysanthemums; the taste of tomatoes and peas and raspberries; the feeling of rough cinders under my feet; the voices of other gardeners, of children yelling far off on the fields. I remembered the factory sirens that wailed at lunchtime, the smell of frying chips from the houses on Windy Ridge. I remembered digging in the dirt with a spoon as an infant, with a spade as a growing boy. I remembered sweat and dirt, blisters on my palms, the sting of sunburn on my neck. I remembered worms and centipedes and beetles, the feeling of them as they moved across an open hand. I remembered the pigeons that wheeled in close, fast flocks over our heads, racing back to the pigeon lofts higher up the hill. Over everything, when I recalled that garden and those days, I heard from high above the endless lovely singing of the larks.

Budding writers often ask for advice. What books must be read? What writing practice must be done? Well, there are libraries full of books to be read and reams of notepaper to be filled, and there are great joys and great benefits to be found in the process. But writing isn't a skill like, say, tennis is – a skill that can be strengthened and refined by constant rehearsal of particular moves, constant development of particular muscles. If you do nothing but write in preparation for writing you'll become a very dismal writer. Listening to larks while digging with a spoon in the dirt might look like a kid just mucking about, but in the long run it can be as valuable as a couple of hours extra homework with pen in hand or fingers on the keyboard.

There are other, darker forces at work in *Wild Girl, Wild Boy*, of course. My father died when I was young and when my sisters were much younger. So Elaine's pain is something that I know about. But her story is one of life, not death. She's a bold creative spirit, brave enough to yell and scream at death, brave enough to outface it, brave enough to keep returning to her wilderness and to discover – or create – the means to transcend her pain. This is what the writer does: explore the gardens of the mind, crawl through wilderness, emerge with scratched skin and muddied knees accompanied by words and creatures and images that begin to form themselves into the stories that help to keep the world alive.

Printed stories usually take the form of prose: blocks of print that start at the top left-hand corner of a page, march line by line down to the bottom right, then jump up to the top left again. They're the product of solitary days and weeks and months of scribbling in notebooks, tapping at the keyboard, staring out of the window, hissing in frustration, dreaming, pondering, scribbling again, tapping again, slowly slowly trying to sort a wild tangle of words and notions into a coherent story. In the end, all those lovely lines of print and all those lovely pages look beautifully organised, beautifully controlled.

When I was a boy, and beginning to dream of becoming an author, printed pages were both an inspiration and a hindrance to me. I found them beautiful and I wanted to produce them, but at the same time their beauty intimidated me – they seemed so fixed, so untouchable, the writer who produced them must have such an organised mind. How could I, whose mind seemed a jumble, dare to think that I could do the same?

The fixity of a book, and the static beauty of a printed page, are illusions. A printed story is just a story caught between covers at a particular time. Caught earlier or later, the story would have a different form. And the untouchable beauty of the page is the work of the typesetter, printer, publisher.

Any good story, no matter how controlled it appears on the page, is not a tame trapped thing. It still has wildness in it, a yearning to break free of its neat lines and numbered pages. And it does break free. It leaps from the page, and moves far beyond the control of the author, as soon as a reader begins to read it.

Reading is a creative, imaginative act. The reader helps to create the book. Each reader creates a different book. Each reader hears different voices, sees different faces and landscapes. Their reading of the book is infected by their own experiences, expectations, dreams and desires. A story is a living thing that escapes from the page and races and prowls through our imaginations.

A play can have even fewer claims to fixity. I began to

write *Wild Girl, Wild Boy* as I would a piece of prose – alone in my study in Newcastle. I imagined the empty space, the stage. I began to write Elaine's words. I had a notion of what Elaine looked like, how she sounded, what her room looked like, what her estate looked like, what her mum and dad looked like, how they sounded ... They walked and talked and danced in the stage-like space I'd cleared in my mind.

But unlike stories in prose that march line by line from top left to bottom right, all the space filled in by the writer, a story in play form moves down the page in short bursts surrounded by lots of space. Dialogue, names, skimpy stage directions, and that's all. The space around the words is for the director, the actors and the designer to fill.

Pretty soon I was out of my study with a half-finished script and on the train to London to see what would happen to this story when it started to break free.

We workshopped the script in an empty space in Islington; Pop-Up Theatre's director, Mike Dalton; assistant director, Jane Wolfson; four actors; and myself. As soon as the lines were spoken, they became something new – at once very like and very unlike the way I'd heard them in my mind. And each time they were re-spoken, they changed again. I saw what happened in silence in a reader's mind happening in a stage-like space before me.

The story was taking on a new life, was being recreated. It had begun to break away and to prowl through the imaginations of everybody there. Elaine leapt to life, became a real girl in front of me, no longer a notion on a page and in my mind, but a dancing, crawl-ing, singing, yelling character of flesh and blood born not just from my words but from the skills of an actor.

Rewriting was an active and immediate act. If a character's words fell flat we tried out other variations of the words. The half-finished script was soon filled with scribbled notes: my own responses, the responses of the directors and the actors.

We had particular discussions about the character McNamara. In the early draft he was a one-dimensional cardboard cut out: simply sinister, nothing more. I was amazed when an actor showed me how his lines could be spoken to suggest a greater complexity, that there was potential to turn McNamara into a slightly more sympathetic (and believable) character. McNamara remains a sinister force, of course, but I hope I learned to suggest that there might be some true concern and tenderness in him.

I watched and listened and scribbled and discussed and learned. I took my script home, scribbled, pondered, contemplated the stage-space in my mind, reworked, wrote on. I maintained an ongoing e-mail correspondence with Mike Dalton in which we shared our suggestions, our excitements, our doubts. Like a good editor commenting on a story in prose, he was able to pinpoint where a tiny adjustment in particular places would benefit the story overall.

We workshopped again. There were difficulties with pacing, with the sequencing of events. There were clumsy moments. How could we make the chorus of voices work on stage? How could we make the shifts from present to past convincing? I scribbled again, wrote again, the story developed again.

By the time we reached rehearsals, we had the first movements of James Hesford's and Mark Pearson's amazingly atmospheric and evocative music. We had the first mock-up of Will Hargreaves' set: a magical thing that could blend Elaine's bedroom with her dad's allotment with a doctor's surgery, that could evoke the movements of Elaine's restless, yearning mind. We also had a cast: Janet Bamford, Mark Huckett, Andrew Oliver, Mandy Vernon-Smith. Here they were, the people who would finally lift the story from my pages and pass it over to an audience. These actors stepped into the story, danced in it, sang in it, laughed and cried in it, made it their own world. The story was recreated yet again.

By now, the script was just about done: only a few adjustments remained, to make the words flow more easily and rhythmically on the tongue and on the air. More and more, I became an observer. Moment by moment, the story moved further away from me.

I left it there, in the rehearsal space in Islington, and went home again to Newcastle to work on other projects. For *Wild Girl, Wild Boy*, as far as I was concerned, all that remained were a couple of e-mail messages, a couple of phone calls with Mike. While I sat at my desk, the music and the set were completed, the play moved from the space in Islington into a week's rehearsal in its first venue, The Lyric Studio.

I travelled nervously to the first performance. I

trembled a little as I went into the theatre. An hour before the performance, I opened the door into the dark studio, stepped inside. A last-minute rehearsal was under way. The music played. Beneath the stage lights were the bedroom, the allotment. The moon shone through the window above the bed. Who was that figure that shuffled through the lights, with his wild hair, his ragged clothes, with fur on his hands and feet? Who was that girl, her face transfigured by a weird mixture of despair and delight?

I only paused there for a few astonished seconds, but in those seconds I looked into a world that I'd helped to create, but that no longer needed me. I stepped back through the door, into the everyday light, and waited with the rest of the audience for the first performance to begin.

In the weeks and months that followed, the play travelled across the country. It appeared in theatres, arts centres, school halls. While I got on with my life in Newcastle, Skoosh came out from the wilderness in Manchester, Elaine wept and yelled in Stirling, McNamara announced his theories on child-raising in Aberystwyth, Dad planted fairies in Hemel Hempstead, Mum nibbled raspberries in Brighton. The set was erected, taken down, erected again, the cast travelled hundreds of miles, the music was played and replayed, the stage-spaces were illuminated and then returned to darkness. The audiences came and watched and went home again. The story ran its course and ran its course again until the tour was over.

In the end, of course, none of it exists. There is no Elaine, there is no Wild Boy, there is no allotment, there is no bedroom. The play is a subterfuge, a set of disguises and tricks. It's a pack of lies. The story of Elaine and Skoosh exists in the minds of those that see the story on the stage, and of those that read their story on the page.

Like all stories, it's a pack of lies that tries to reach out to us and allow us to experience some kind of human truth. Of course it depends on the creative skills of writer, directors, actors, composers, designers. But it also depends on the creative skills of the audience, those skills of the imagination that allow all of us to leap into other minds and other worlds, skills that are at once quite natural, straightforward, commonplace and quite quite amazing.

D. A.